Dear Santa, Thanks for the Piano

Rose-Mary Rumbley

Illustrations by Chuck Fisher

EAKIN PRESS ✦ Fort Worth, Texas
www.EakinPress.com

I Dedicate This Book To:

One of my favorite students, who now is a fine
pianist/organist, Jeff Herrick, graduate of Dallas
Baptist University;
and to
my favorite piano teacher, piano soloist, and true
artist at the piano, Sue Mitz, Professor of Piano,
Dallas Baptist University

An Introduction

Along with the new millennium comes the 300th birthday of the piano, an instrument that the renowned composer Ferruccio Busoni termed "the best actor in the company of instruments." Piano virtuoso Arthur Rubinstein went on to say, "A piano is not just one instrument—it is a hundred." The piano has served not only as a music provider, but it has also had political merits. The piano united Germany before Bismarck. It was an Italian, Bartolomeo Cristofori, who invented the valued instrument, but the Germans got together and perfected it.

But let's go back to 1700, when the piano first came upon the scene. It conquered Europe! Everyone who was anyone learned to play the piano—kings, queens, clergy, servants, ditch diggers—all could play. There was a gilded, ornate piano in every castle, and a simple, unadorned one in the more modest dwellings.

Of course, later the piano came to the New World—the United States of America. City homes, as well as those out on the farms all along the Eastern Seaboard, had pianos in their parlors. But the piano didn't stop in the East. It conquered the West!

The 49ers went toward the setting sun with their hearts filled with dreams of finding gold and becoming rich. Their covered wagons were filled with needed supplies, and often there would be a piano crammed in the middle of the kitchen utensils. Out west, every town had a couple of saloons, and in almost every one of these saloons, including the Long Branch in Dodge City, where Sheriffs Wyatt Earp and Bat

Masterson hung out, there was a piano. Some pretty tough *hombres* would wander into town and shoot off a couple of rounds. The piano player often had to duck the bullets, but during these gunfights he never missed a note. I recall those episodes in the old westerns on TV. Guns were blazing, bullets were flying, but the piano music never stopped during those exciting and sometimes deadly moments.

Writers have been most complimentary of the piano. Prim and proper Jane Austen wrote of the women in high society who always studied piano. They did so because they were expected to entertain their company at home. The piano served as an aid to courtship.

The lady and her beau could be alone in the parlor without a chaperone as long as the music was playing. Nothing serious could be going on if one of the couple was busy playing the piano.

Before the days of Miss Austen, Voltaire and Rousseau, highly respected authors during the 18th century, both termed the piano "The highest form of musical language."

But alas, the piano has had to take a lot of abuse along with all the praise. It was Robert Schumann, magnificent musician, who shouted one day after a long practice session, "I would like to smash my piano to pieces!" His threat sounded more fateful and more menacing when spoken in German.

Franz Liszt played so hard and loud on his piano, he broke the strings! Beethoven had such

a temper that in 1805 the music director of the Royal Theatre in Vienna, Count Palffy, shut down Beethoven's opera, *Fidelio,* because Beethoven yelled at the piano!

There has not only been verbal abuse, but also some physical abuse directed at the piano. What about all those singers who've perched on the piano during their performances? Some of those roosting songbirds were skinny, but a lot of them were on the heavy side. Such a strain it was on that box that housed the melodious strings!

The piano has been in the middle of hot competition. One contest was legendary. In 1717 Johann Sebastian Bach was to play opposite the Frenchman Louis Marchand. It was actually a political rally. Surely the German would trounce the Frenchman. Marchand was dressed to the hilt in his purple court attire. He retired to the dressing room, but when it came time for the competition, he was nowhere to be found. Bach won by default. There is still a German expression used for a hasty retreat: One leaves his compliments in French. In other words, a German who departs quickly will say, "I'm out of here!" in French. Germans get the humor behind the statement!

There was the contest between Cavalier Allessandro Scarlatti and Georg Friedrich Handel. Later, Bach was invited too. The amazing thing about these three musicians— they were all born the same year, 1685. And they were so busy, they were unable to come to the competition, so I guess we can say they all three won. It's best that way for sure.

Another contest was held in Vienna in 1781. This match was between Muzio Clementi and

Mozart. The audience was divided. Mozart, always the egotist, declared himself the winner over Clementi. But Clementi got the last word. Mozart, who was twenty-five years old at the time, lived only ten more years. Clementi survived him by more than forty-five years. In fact, Clementi later gave up performing and became a partner to the London piano maker Collard. Clementi also became a publisher and secured the right to publish Beethoven's works in England.

The most famous piano competition today is held in Fort Worth, Texas, every four years. It's the Van Cliburn International Piano Competition, which started in 1962, just after the lanky, twenty-three-year-old talented Texan won the Tchaikovsky International Competition. Everyone present at that contest assumed a Russian would win. The judges feared being sent to Siberia if anyone but a Russian would win. But Premier Nikita Khrushchev asked, "Who is the best?" The answer came: "The Texan!" "Then let the Texan win!" shouted the Soviet leader, and Van was declared the winner!

Pianos make wonderful Christmas gifts. This was certainly what piano maker Thomas Broadwood thought. In December 1817 he sent one of his magnificent grands to Beethoven, who was almost completely deaf by then. Nevertheless, when the gift from England arrived, Beethoven was pleased with the fine quality of the piano.

My grandfather also thought a piano would make a great gift for his little girl, my mother. It was Christmas 1903 when my mother received her piano from her father. She was so proud of the gift, and she started lessons immediately.

Mother lived in downtown Dallas, and in 1908 the Trinity River left its banks and the whole city was underwater. Mother said she remembered screaming as the water moved into the house, "My piano! My piano!" My grandfather, with the help of some sturdy men, was able to put the piano on boxes, and the water missed the cherished instrument.

My mother always declared, "Keep that piano. It survived a flood on boxes!" I still have that piano, and I have it tuned regularly. In fact, it was this Christmas piano of Mother's, along with the 300th anniversary of the favored instrument, that prompted me to write this book.

The History

Christmas! It was everywhere, and Jeff, as he walked to school, felt the spirit of the season all over the neighborhood. He skipped along singing his favorite Christmas carol, "Joy to the World."

In no time at all, he was in the schoolhouse opening his locker. He crammed his coat and lunch into the tiny space and rushed on to class. He sat down at his desk just as Miss Jenkins, his teacher, was coming into the room.

With excitement in her voice, Miss Jenkins said, "My dear students, I have a surprise for you today."

The class loved surprises. When you're in the fourth grade, you always love surprises.

"Today, I'm going to tell you a story."

So what! thought the members of the class. After all, Miss Jenkins told lots of stories.

"I am going to tell you the story of the piano. That's right, I will tell you all about that very popular musical instrument." She paused for a second. "And I have a reason for telling the story. You see, today—this very day—the piano is 300 years old!"

So what! thought the class again. *What's so important about the piano?*

But after they heard the story, the kids changed their "tune" about this instrument that was so familiar to them all. There was one large grand piano in the school auditorium, and there was another one—an upright—in the music room. Their feelings changed because the story of this instrument—the piano—is quite interesting and absorbing. Here is how Miss Jenkins told it:

In ancient times, man spent a lot of his days hunting for food. Wives kept the home fires burning, and men went out to provide the meat for the table. The bow and arrow were invented by early man to assist in the hunt. The bow was an arched stick of wood with animal gut strung across to hold the bend in the stick. The arrow was made with another stick that had one end whittled into a sharp point. The arrow was set onto the drawn bow, and when the gut string was released, the arrow would soar forward. As time passed, man became more and more skilled in the use of his bow. He never missed his target!

One day, a man strolling down the trail happened upon his supper—it could have been anything from a rabbit to a deer. He quickly drew back the bow, and the arrow swiftly snapped forward. The animal

gut of the bow gave out a loud *twang* as the arrow sailed into the heart of the animal destined for the evening's meal. The man took the "supper" animal home for his wife to cook. While he was eating the roasted "whatever," he remembered the *twang*. He couldn't get the sound out of his head. It was a haunting sound. It was music!

Man then began to add more strings to his bow, and soon he had a musical instrument—the harp! The angels had been strumming on harps in heaven always, but now man had created the instrument that could produce the heavenly sounds.

One of the earliest harpists in recorded history was King David of Jerusalem. He was the music director at the temple. He wrote inspiring psalms for the church service and for private worship. David sang while he played the harp. David also played and composed music for the pipes—better known as the flute.

In fact, King David could play all of the instruments—harp, flute, trumpet, bells, cymbals, drums, and a fairly new one, the dulcimer. Ah, the dulcimer! It was a stringed instrument like the harp, but instead of plucking the strings, the musician would strike the strings with a hammer. This action produced an entirely different sound. Five hundred years after King David's rule, around 550 B.C., a civilization known as Greece rose up. The Greeks, like David's people, the children of Israel, were brilliant. One such smart Greek was Pythagoras, who was interested in mathematics, especially in relation to weights and measures. He was known for the Pythagorean theorem, a theorem used in algebra: $a^2 + b^2 = c^2$.

But he was also into music, because it was Pythagoras who discovered from his travels to Egypt and India that if the strings of the harp and the dulcimer were shortened, the instruments would produce different sounds—different pitches.

Two hundred years later, the Greeks, still very much interested in music, created a water organ with pipes. But instead of a man blowing through the pipes, the wind was forced through them by the pressure of water. And to force the wind to come through, a "key" was hit that moved a lever to do the work. These keys were large, and they were hit by the whole hand in a leather glove. Ctesibius, a Greek from Alexandria, a city on the delta of the Nile River, was credited for inventing the keys.

Years and years later, during the Christian era, music from the organ was produced in a different manner. The organ was no longer hydraulic, because the wind came from bellows. Winchester Cathedral in 1093 had a magnificent organ. By 1350 a monk in Poland built an organ with a full chromatic scale, and in 1361, a German priest, Nicholas Faber, finished the famous organ at Halberstadt with the keys connected to the pipes. The size of the keys got smaller as time passed.

While the organ had keys, the psaltery (harp)

and the dulcimer did not. The strings on the harp were plucked, and the strings of the dulcimer were struck with hammers. Time marched on, and there were more and more strings, more and more plucking, and more and more striking, and finally, borrowing from the organ, the keys were added. What was called a "harpsichord" came into being. One pressed the keys, the keys activated levers, and those levers plucked the strings.

Edward III of England, to prove that he was every inch a king, invaded France in 1330. And so began that disastrous period of hostilities that was to be known as the Hundred Years War. At first, things went well with England. In fact, King John of France was captured. While John was in prison, Edward had a harpsichord brought to his cell so he could entertain himself. Obviously, the harpsichord had caught on, and many, many people could play. King John of France was thankful for some "high toned" recreation while in jail.

The poet Geoffrey Chaucer was in the English army and was captured while fighting in France. Edward III valued him highly enough to pay a part of his ransom. In Chaucer's *Canterbury Tales*, in "The Miller's Tale," the poet pays tribute to the miller's harp:

Above his bed lay a gallant harp in sight
On which he played melodiously at night
With such a touch that all the chamber rang;
It was the Virgin's Angelus he sang,
And after that he sang King William's Note,
And people often blessed his merry throat.

By 1404, in France, there was an instrument created, the clavicordium, whose strings were hit by hammers when one pressed the keys. So, with that invention, the world actually had two types of "keyed" stringed instruments—the harpsichord, with plucked strings, and the clavicordium, with struck strings. However, both instruments were considered part of the harpsichord family.

Each country had its own name for this stringed instrument. In England and in the Netherlands, because lovely maidens played the harpsichord, it was called a virginal.

In 1502 Henry VII and his wife, Elizabeth of York, sponsored a pageant that featured twelve lovely ladies playing virginals!

Henry VIII played the virginal, as did his two daughters, Mary and Elizabeth. The Catholic queen, Mary Queen of Scots, played the virginal until her head was chopped off by Elizabeth. Mary's son, James I, who became king after Elizabeth and is known for his sponsorship of the new translation of the Bible, also enjoyed playing the virginal.

The son of James I, Charles I, was beheaded by the Puritans, because he wasn't "pure"— at least not according to them. Before his head rolled, he enjoyed "virginal" music, which was considered first-class impurity by the Puritan leaders.

From 1640 to 1660, Oliver Cromwell, totally

"pure," led England, and there was no music, no theatre, no fun! The Puritans felt that if one was having a great time, one was sinning!

But after the Puritan regime ended and after the Stuarts were restored to the throne, Charles II, known as the "Merry Monarch," brought back music, and singing and playing the virginal once again became part of the daily life in England. Show biz flourished. There was a father and son act— Thomas and John Hitchcock. They appeared nightly on the stage in London. They were sensational virginal players who "wowed" their audiences for years.

In Italy the harpsichord became known as a "spinet," because Giovanni Spinetti, a Venetian, played the instrument so beautifully.

In 1581 a Dutchman, Hans Ruckers, painted the lid of the harpsichord, thus introducing a special kind of art into the making of the instrument.

Italian prince Ferdinando de Medici, son of the Grand Duke Cosimo III of Tuscany, was a skilled harpsichord player. He visited the city of Padua in 1689. There he stopped in at the shop of Bartolomeo Cristofori, who was working to perfect the old clavicordium. Cristofori was able to make its hammer action much quicker. The velocity of the hammer responding to the touch of the player was the chief feature. The variation in velocity meant that Cristofori's instrument could be played either softly or loudly, thus the name *pianoforte*, Italian for "soft-loud." As time went on, the "forte" was dropped and the name "piano" was given to the instrument. This is quite ironic, since modern pianos are much louder than the original ones were. Maybe we should have called the piano a "forte" instead.

There was another unusual feature. After going down for the strike, the hammer raised up to its fullest height. Thus, the strings were free to vibrate. The sound was not stifled. Cristofori had made huge improvements to the instrument!

Cristofori died in 1731, and his student, Giovanni Ferrini, continued his work. Ferrini made a piano in 1730 for the queen of Spain, Elizabetta Farnese.

But Italian interest in the piano began to fade. The Germans took over. Gottfried Silbermann made two instruments for Bach in 1736. In

1747 Bach visited Frederick the Great in Potsdam at the castle of Sans Souci, and there he discovered a couple of Silbermann pianos—German made.

About one hundred years later, born in Germany, there was a young man who began to make pianos. When one hears his name, one instantly thinks of fine pianos. His name was Henry Steinway!

Miss Jenkins finished the story. The children had sopped up the information like little sponges. Their faces beamed. The story of the piano was most engaging!

"Gotta Have One"

After hearing the great story of the piano, Jeff rushed home. "Mother, Mother, I must start taking piano lessons immediately." He was so excited his mother didn't understand a word spitting from his lips.

"What are you saying?"

Jeff took a deep breath. "I'm saying that I must start taking piano lessons immediately!"

"What brought this on?" Mother sat down to hear the whole story.

"Miss Jenkins, our music teacher, told us about the piano. Did you know the piano is 300 years old today?"

"Oh, really?" Mother tried to sound thrilled. "So what does that have to do with you?"

"Well, everything about the piano is so exciting. Mother, I must start taking lessons now! Now! Okay?"

His mother sighed deeply. "We don't have a piano."

Jeff's face lit up. "I want a piano for Christmas. That's all I want—a piano!"

"All! Do you realize that pianos are very, very expensive?" His mother tried to be understanding.

"That I know. So, that's why I want just a piano. Nothing else. Just a piano! Please!"

The Purchase

That weekend Jeff and his mother went down to the piano store. All the kids must have thought the story was exciting, because there was a long, long line of kids with their parents in the store. There was a rush on pianos!

"Why are so many people here?" shouted Mother.

"Because the piano is 300 years old, and we all want pianos!" everyone in the store answered in a grand chorus.

Mother was almost speechless. She just said, "Oh."

Nevertheless, she waited with Jeff for their turn to buy a piano. They selected a fine piano, and the salesman suggested a teacher for Jeff, who was completely happy! He was going to have his own piano.

The Delivery

Meanwhile, up at the North Pole, Santa Claus was buried in requests for pianos. Elves did not know how to make pianos, so Santa sent out emergency orders to all the piano makers in the world. The pianos came in, and Santa was thrilled when he realized he had enough pianos to fill the wishes of all the kids. But he still had a big, big problem. "How am I going to deliver these huge, heavy instruments?" he wondered. He was going to have to come up with some ingenious plan.

After some serious thought, Santa came up with the solution. He was definitely going to need two sleighs—one for toys and one for the pianos. Santa had a spare sleigh, so there was no problem there, but where was he going to get the extra reindeer?

Surely reindeer were available. He needed not

eight tiny ones, but twelve husky, hearty ones. After all, they were going to be piano movers!

The next day, word came from the Reindeer Music Conservatory. "You need reindeer? We're on our way!" The message was brief but to the point.

The reindeer arrived. Their names were Bach, Mozart, Beethoven, Liszt, Schubert, Schumann, Horowitz Chopin, Rachmaninoff, Rubinstein, Paderewski, and Van Cliburn!

Because of their musical backgrounds, they were eager to pull the sleigh laden with pianos. They assured Santa that the pianos would be delivered on time.

Obviously, the reindeer were named for well-known composers and pianists. Here is some background information about their namesakes.

Reindeer Bach

Named for the greatest baroque composer!

Johann Sebastian Bach, born in Eisenach, Germany, in 1685, was one of those people who made up his mind, and that was it! He was conducting the church orchestra one day, and he decided that the bassoonist sounded like a goat. "That's not music! That's a goat!" he exclaimed. A fight broke out. Bach drew a knife! But fortunately, no one was hurt. The master composer calmed down.

Tired of working for a certain duke, Bach quit his job as royal musician. The duke was so mad, he threw Bach in jail. There in the jail cell, the master composer wrote forty-six pieces of music that musicians still play to this day.

But despite his temper, Bach was a loving father. What else could he be? He had twenty children, and he adored every one of them. Naturally, Bach had to work very hard to support this large family. He played for the church. He composed for the church. He was always busy making money to put food on the table. When he was at home with the family, there was always a baby on his lap. He bounced the baby while he drank his favorite drink—coffee! He even wrote a cantata about coffee!

Every beginning pianist learns Bach's Two-Part Inventions. Inventions are ideas, and Bach had many of them. He died in Leipzig, Germany, in 1750.

Reindeer Mozart
Named for a child prodigy!

Born in Salzburg in 1756, baby Wolfgang Amadeus Mozart climbed on the piano and played a piece his sister had been working on. Then, at four years old, he composed a piece for himself. By the age of five, he was practicing all day and way into the night. At six he played for royalty, and at seven he proposed to Queen Marie Antoinette. He was eight when he composed his first symphony and only eleven when he composed his first opera. By the way, he could also play the violin!

The young Mozart performed all over Europe. After each performance, everyone in the audience craved to come up and kiss him. He was the most kissed person in the world!

Mozart married and had six children, but only two lived to adulthood. His schedule ran like this: up at six, compose until nine, give music lessons until one. Then he'd go out to eat at a friend's house, where, of course, he had to entertain. Talk about singing for your supper! Mozart played constantly for his.

Unfortunately, Mozart spent more money than he made, so he died a pauper. He was often rude to people, so he also died friendless. He was not a hale and hearty person, so with all the concerts, composing, and teaching, he died very, very young in Vienna in 1791.

Reindeer Beethoven
Named for an ill-mannered composer!

Ludwig van Beethoven, born in Bonn, Germany, in 1770, studied piano with his father when he was four years old. His father would rap little Ludwig's knuckles if he were not playing the piece correctly. The rapping must have been taken as an encouragement, because by the time Beethoven was twelve, he was playing at court— for money! This was good, because his father really never was able to make a living for the family.

Beethoven became the most celebrated pianist of the time. Still, he often displayed extremely temperamental behavior. If someone in the audience would cough or sneeze, Beethoven would stop playing.

He was not very good-looking, and to add to his ugliness, he was very, very sloppy. To be blunt, he looked like a bum. Once he was actually arrested as a bum. The police couldn't believe it was Beethoven.

He never married. No woman could live with such sloppiness. He wrote the Moonlight Sonata for a woman. Still, this charming piece could not woo her to become interested in Ludwig.

All his life, he needed and wanted applause. His troubled life came to an end in Vienna in 1827.

Reindeer Liszt
Named for the first concert pianist!

Franz Liszt, born in Hungary in 1811, had everything. He had looks, talent, charm. He could remember every piece he ever played, and he was known as the first true concert pianist. He played not only his own works, but also the compositions of other composers. He made certain that the concert pianist was not just an entertainer—he was a maestro!

Liszt often drove his audiences into fits. Ladies threw jewels at him. Once, two countesses staged a wrestling match in order to approach him.

All the royalty in Europe were entertained by Franz Liszt. His final tour ended in April 1886 with a concert for Queen Victoria at the Grand Crystal Palace in London. He promised he would come back, but he died the following July.

Reindeer Schubert
Named for a short-lived composer!

The very musical Franz Schubert was born in Vienna in 1797, and he died there—very young— in 1828.

Little Franz was such a brilliant musician that he stood out in the band at the music school he attended. The conductor of the band asked, "Who is it who is playing so cleverly?" Of course, it was the small boy with the spectacles—Franz Schubert!

He composed a very outstanding mass with loud praises to the Lord. This startled the members of the parish.

Because he loved to sing, he composed not only praise songs but operas, as well. Symphonies and sonatas were also added to his credits.

Unfortunately, Schubert was never able to finish some of the work he started. He was in poor health most of his life.

He adored the novels of James Fenimore Cooper. He owned every book written by the beloved author. He ordered Cooper's latest novel in 1828, received it, but never finished reading it.

Also, that year he started a symphony, but he never finished it, either. There is a standard joke among musical comedians. "You know Schubert's Unfinished Symphony? Well, I'm going to finish it!"

Reindeer Schumann
Named for an unfriendly composer!

Composer and fine pianist Robert Schumann, born in Zwickau, Saxony, in 1810, was addicted to his diary. He kept a record of everything—his debts, his food intake, the books he read, the hours he practiced, the pieces he practiced. He wrote and played the piano like he was possessed. His father, a preacher, and his mother, the daughter of a surgeon, never encouraged his musical talent. They only urged him to keep writing!

Robert had some fairly strange ideas. He thought that if he bound his index finger in some way, it would make his third finger stronger. This didn't work. Instead, the middle finger stiffened.

Robert Schumann was not a friendly person.

One day someone knocked at the door. He yelled out of the window, "I'm not at home!"

His one friend came to see him one day and received the same treatment. The friend rang the bell. He could hear Schumann playing the piano inside, but the response was rather nasty. Schumann opened the door and said, "Oh, it's you. I'm not at home!"

In spite of all this, he composed beautiful music. The great musician Liszt wrote to musician Hector Berlioz: "Our ingenious Schumann has written some enchanting scenes of children. Schumann is a soulful poet and a great musician."

Robert Schumann died in Bonn, Germany, at the age of 46 years.

Reindeer Horowitz
Named for a famous Russian pianist!

Vladimir Horowitz, a fine pianist, was first taught to play by his mother in Russia, where he was born in 1903. When he finished his studies at the Kiev Conservatory, he traveled to Berlin to play in 1926, to Paris in 1928, and to the White House and President Herbert Hoover in 1931.

In 1933 Horowitz married Arturo Toscanini's

daughter. He continued his touring, always declaring that his idol was Rachmaninoff.

During World War II, Horowitz gave a concert in Central Park. For an encore he played "The Stars and Stripes Forever." This piece then became his permanent encore!

Once when he was playing at Carnegie Hall, he heard that the line for tickets extended over two blocks. He had coffee served to those fans who were waiting in line.

He flew to Russia for a concert in 1986, taking his own piano tuner and chef!

In 1989 Horowitz suddenly died of a heart attack. He is buried in the Toscanini plot in Milan, Italy.

Reindeer Chopin
His namesake composed only for the piano!

Frederic Chopin was born in Poland in 1810. He lived most of his adult life in Paris, but he never forgot his native country. In fact, when he left Poland, he took with him a silver cup of Polish soil. This dirt was poured on his grave when he was buried in Paris in 1849.

Frederic was pale and handsome like his music. Many thought of him as angelic, but he had a mean streak in him. When he played and someone in the audience went to sleep, he'd play a loud *BANG*! to wake up the drifting individual.

Frederic was odd—an eccentric. He always had his houseshoes in a certain spot by his bed, he only ate certain foods, and he despised surprises.

A friend introduced him to the writer Aurore Audevant, a woman who was known as George Sand. They met and sparks flew. They were very much in love. Frederic wrote the famous Minute Waltz for George Sand's dog.

Chopin made money teaching royalty, so he was able to live in luxury. He liked it that way!

This great musician, known as the pianist with the "velvet fingers," composed as much as he could, even though he was never in good health. Chopin often said, "The piano is my second self."

Reindeer Paderewski
His namesake was a stylish pianist!

Someone once said to Paderewski, "There's a rich soul who plays polo." The great composer swiftly replied, "I'm a poor Pole who plays solo!"

Paderewski was born in Poland in 1860, and he was poor. But not for long! He studied piano in Warsaw, went on his first tour in 1876, returned to teach piano at the Warsaw Conservatory, studied in Berlin, went on another tour, and came back a total success!

In 1891 he toured the U.S., beginning that tour with a concert in Carnegie Hall.

Unlike Beethoven, Paderewski was handsome, and everyone loved his appearance. He had long, golden red hair, which he tossed back in grand style.

Speaking of style, he loved to travel that way—in style. He had a private car (on the train) with a bedroom and a practice room. He traveled with his own chef and piano tuner.

In 1914 Paderewski rushed back to Poland to raise money for the Polish Relief Fund. He stayed in his native country and became the first president of the Polish Republic. He unified the contending political parties. After World War I, he returned to America to tour. He died in New York City in 1941.

Reindeer Rachmaninoff
Named for a somber pianist!

Paderewski had long golden curls that he tossed about, while Sergei Rachmaninoff had his hair cut like a convict's. He was known as "the

Puritan Pianist"! He was very somber and seldom showed any theatrical flair when he played. But he was a master at the piano!

At nine years of age, Rachmaninoff, who was born in Russia in 1873, entered the St. Petersburg Conservatory to study music. In 1892 he won the coveted Gold Medal for performance. In 1899 he performed in England.

Rachmaninoff left his native country during the Russian Revolution. Even though he always claimed to be a strong Russian, he returned to Russia only to give concerts. America was his home. He died in Beverly Hills in 1943.

Reindeer Rubinstein
Named for a great Polish pianist!

Arthur Rubinstein, born in Poland in 1887, played a piano concert in 1975 at the age of eighty-eight. The stage was covered with red and white carnations—Poland's colors. The audience shouted, "May he live a hundred years!" He played encore after encore and finally ended the evening with Chopin's Polonaise in A-flat. All Polish people cheer at the mere mention of that piece!

Rubinstein always said he was emotionally attached to his piano. He was a young lad when he started touring all over the world. He was the first interpreter of Chopin.

This renowned piano virtuoso spoke all the European languages, thus making himself the favorite guest at all parties. Besides that, he could play the piano!

In 1974 Rubinstein won the International Piano Competition in Jerusalem.

He wrote two books: *My Young Years*, published in 1973, and *My Many Years*, published in 1980. He died in Geneva in 1982 at the age of ninety-five. He almost lived a hundred years!

Reindeer Van Cliburn
Named for a sensational American pianist!

Van Cliburn was born in Shreveport, Louisiana, in 1934. His beloved mother, Rildia Bee, was his first and only piano teacher until he went to Julliard to study in 1951.

Van was four years old when he gave his first concert. Everyone in the audience knew he was extremely talented, and this was proven when he won the Tchaikovsky Piano Competition in Russia in 1958. Van Cliburn then became world famous!

In 1989 Gorbachev invited Van back to Russia for a concert. He was once again a sensation.

Today, Van resides in Fort Worth, Texas. He played for the opening of the great Bass Hall there. By the way, he also played for the opening of the Morton Meyerson Symphony Hall in Dallas!

Santa hitched up his twelve musical and husky reindeer, and in a flash—they were off!

On Bach, on Mozart, on Beethoven and Liszt.
    Please travel quickly. No child must be
    missed.
On Schubert, on Schumann, on Horowitz and
    Chopin. Cliburn is pulling hard. His
    friends call him Van.
On Rachmaninoff, on Rubinstein, and on
    Paderewski. A Christmas piano beneath
    every tree!
You're fulfilling our dreams with miraculous
    speed! "Bravo!" Santa booms, "You 'dears'
    answered my need!"
Pianos delivered all over the earth! Carols will
    be played. Hallelujah! Such mirth!
Joy is in store when a piano comes your way.
    Happy tunes to you all—and a "grand"
    Christmas Day!

Ode to a Piano Tuner

Oh, exalted piano tuner! You come with ears so perfectly pitched.

You act in mysterious ways. You make sure that when struck, three strings create one note. Are you bewitched?

Certainly not! It just seems that way because of your enormous strength.

Turn those hitchpins, which hook the strings. Pitch is determined by tension as well as length!

Piano tuning is not dull. A tuner can crop up in many a place—on boats, in barns, mansions, the Paris subway, or a roller rink.

Audiences are everywhere. Folks eagerly await a pianist to come and offer the ethereal *plink, plunk, plink!*

Alas, a man can get personal about his piano. The tuner is "laying hands" on his prized possession.

He might experience inner harmonies and vibrations himself if his piano is his obsession.

Of course, there's the composer. He's the one who writes for those magnificent eighty-eight.

But if the piano is not in tune, it matters not what he doth create.

Ah, but when the artist bangs out the piece and the piano is very much in tune,

"Bravo! Encore!" the audience shouts. "Come back and play for us again! Please make it soon!"

Bibliography

Books

Blom, Eric. *The Romance of the Piano*. New York: Da Capo Press, 1969.

Goodman, Harriet. *Piano Forte: A History of the Piano*. New York: George Braziller, 1989.

Grover, Dovid S. *The Piano: Its Story from Zither to Grand*. New York: Charles Scribners, 1979.

Grove's Dictionary of Music and Musicians. New York: The MacMillan Company, 1949.

James, Philip. *Early Keyboard Instruments*. London: The Holland Company, 1975.

Krull, Kathleen. *Lives of the Musicians*. NewYork: Harcourt Brace and Company, 1993.

Oringer, Judith. *Passions for the Piano*. Los Angeles: Jeremy P. Tarcher, Inc., 1988.

Parakilas, James. *Piano Roles*. Connecticut: Yale University, 2000.

Ratcliffe, Ronald V. *Steinway and Sons*. San Francisco: Chronical Books, 1989.

Periodicals

Chelminski, Rudolph. "In Praise of the Piano and Artists Who Play Them." *Smithsonian Magazine* (March 2000): 60–72.

CPSIA information can be obtained
at www.ICGtesting.com
Printed in the USA
LVOW13s2356211216
518361LV00031B/344/P